It's another Quality Book from CGP

This book has been carefully written for Key Stage Two children preparing for the reading part of the Year 6 SATs. It's full of tricky questions covering all seven of the reading Assessment Focuses:

- AF1 Understand the **meaning** of a text ← *AF1 isn't specifically tested in the SAT, but it underpins all the other Assessment Focuses.*
- AF2 Select and **retrieve** information
- AF3 **Infer** information and ideas
- AF4 Understand **structural** and **layout** features
- AF5 Understand **language** features
- AF6 Interpret the **writer's purpose**
- AF7 Relate texts to their **context**

In this book we've separated the questions out so children can learn how to spot questions on each Assessment Focus and give exactly the right kind of answer.

Children can use the Reading Raptor tick boxes for self-assessment, which helps you work out how they're getting on with each Assessment Focus.

Published by CGP

Written by: Chris Fenton

Editors: Camilla Simson, Megan Tyler and Rachel Ward.

Many thanks to David Broadbent and Judy Hornigold for proofreading.

With thanks to Laura Collar for copyright research.

Image of the sinking of the Titanic on page 36 by Willy Stoewer © Bettmann/CORBIS

ISBN: 978 1 84146 164 9

Groovy website: www.cgpbooks.co.uk
Jolly bits of clipart from CorelDRAW®
Printed by Elanders Ltd, Newcastle upon Tyne.

Based on the classic CGP style created by Richard Parsons.

The pieces of writing in this booklet are all taken from a book called *Sea Voyages*, edited by Sally McGinty. This is the introduction she wrote for her book:

Introduction

As a young girl, I lived on a tiny Scottish island. There was no school on the island, so every morning a fishing boat came to fetch all the children and take them to school on the mainland. I would sit in the bows, calling out to my friends when I saw seals basking on the rocks.

When I left school I went to work on a cruise ship and sailed round the world five times. Later, I came back to Britain with a family of my own, and we all went to live on a canal boat called *Tulip*.

Today I live on another, much warmer island in the South Pacific. Every journey here is made by boat. If I want to do the shopping, collect the post, or visit my friends I have to sail to another island in my little boat, *Albatross*.

All About Boats — Non-Fiction

The next bit of writing you've got to read is NON-FICTION. That means it's stuffed full of facts. These facts are all about ships, boats and how sailors find their way around the ocean.

What to do —

1) Open out the folding pages and read the non-fiction text *All About Boats*.
2) When you've read it, read it again.
3) Once you've done that, you'll have to walk the plank into the shark-infested waters of... The Questions...

Turn the page ➡

Navigation

When you are out in the middle of the ocean, it's very difficult to know where you are. Everything looks the same — just waves everywhere. It'd be all too easy to go round and round in circles for months...

In The Past, How Did Sailors Know Where They Were?

Sailors have been crossing the oceans of the world for hundreds of years. In the days before modern gadgets were invented, they had to work things out for themselves.

A compass with a magnetic needle would show them which way was North.
They used a 'sextant' to measure the angle of the Sun, to work out how far North or South they were.
At night, their knowledge of the stars meant they had a giant map in the sky, guiding them home.

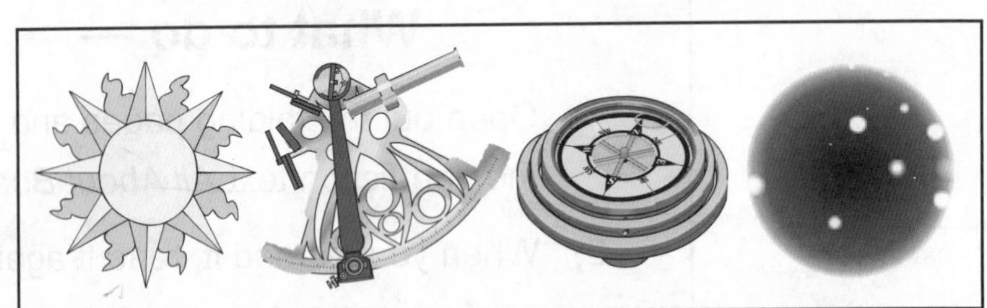

How Do Sailors Know Where They Are Today?

Nowadays, ships use fancy electronic devices to tell them exactly where they are. GPS (Global Positioning System) uses signals from satellites in space to pinpoint the ship's position and radar tells you whether other ships are around.
Of course, we have much better maps now too, showing where the land is, the depth of the sea, and any dangerous rocks, or strong currents.

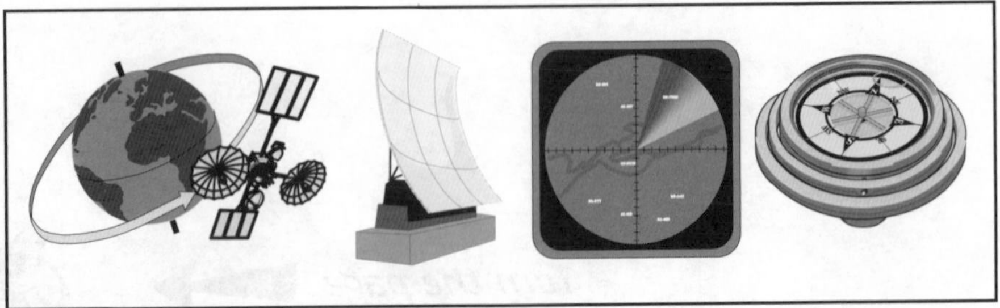

Despite all the fancy gadgets, sailors still carry a good old-fashioned compass — if everything else breaks down, you can rely on a compass.

All About Boats

Galleon

An old fighting ship, with cannons along each side. Lots of sails gave them speed for catching other ships — or for running away!

Tug

A small powerful boat that tugs big ships out of harbour to guide them safely past other ships and out to sea.

Cruise Ship

A huge ship, like a floating hotel, where people enjoy holiday cruises. They can have cinemas, casinos, and even swimming pools!

Canoe

A simple boat, perfect for travelling on lakes, rivers, and on sheltered coastlines. Can easily be carried by one or two people.

Sailing Words

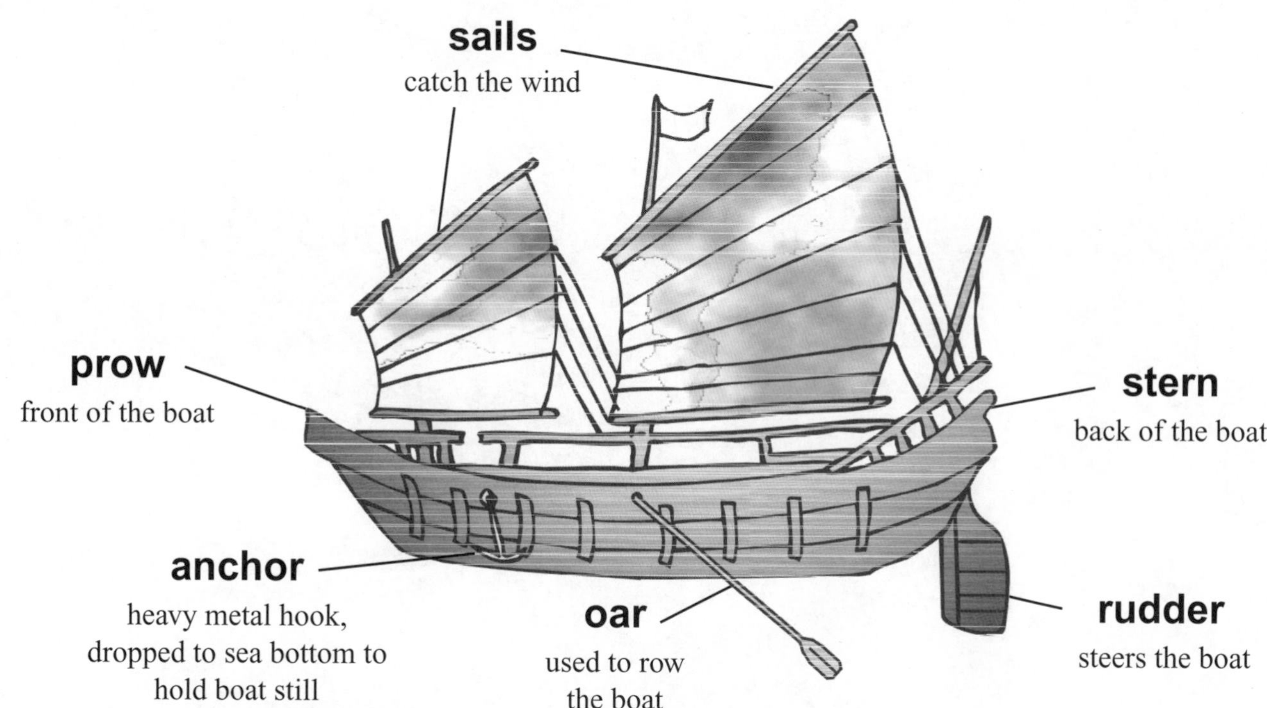

Keep turning...

I decided to put this book together because I wanted to show what it's like living with boats — always about to set out on a new adventure, or happy to be returning home safely from the sea.

My book begins with *All About Boats,* which gives lots of useful information about different kinds of boats and how to sail them.

There are many stories about the sea. Some, like *Jason and the Argonauts*, are myths — the story is probably based on something that really happened, but so many incredible details have been added over the years that it's hard to tell what the original true story is.

The Kon-Tiki Voyage tells a true story about a sailor called Thor Heyerdahl, who wanted to find out whether a myth about another sailor called Kon-Tiki could be true.

Raising a Storm is something I saw in the newspaper a few years ago. It shows how the sea still fascinates people and leads them to do extraordinary (some would say foolish) things.

I hope you enjoy this book as much as I have enjoyed living on and beside the sea.

Sally McGinty
Tahiti, February 2012

Structure and Layout Questions

STRUCTURE and LAYOUT questions ask about the way the writing looks on the page. Keep an eye out for boxes, arrows, subheadings or underlining when you're reading a text. You might get asked about them.

1. Why do you think the writer divided the information about the boats into separate boxes?

   .... **1 mark**

2. Look at the large, labelled diagram of a boat. Explain why some of the words are **larger** than others.

   .... **1 mark**

3. How do the lines help you to understand the information about the different parts of the boat in the diagram?

   .... **1 mark**

4. On the right-hand page, what is the purpose of the subheadings and how do they make the text easier to read?

   .... **2 marks**

   ....

5. If the pictures on page 7 were labelled, do you think this would make the text easier to understand? Answer the question as fully as you can.

   .... **2 marks**

   ....

   ....

Structure and layout questions are a doddle for a Reading Raptor. How did you do?

Inference Questions

Sometimes it's tricky to understand what writers really mean. INFERENCE questions are about showing that you really understand what a writer's on about.

1. Canoes can '**easily be carried by one or two people**'. What does this imply about the weight of a canoe?

.... **1 mark**

2. Apart from a tug boat, name another of the boats that could be called **'powerful'** and explain why.

.... **2 marks**

....

3. What are the main differences between the ways sailors navigated in the past and today?

.... **2 marks**

....

4. What word tells us that Global Positioning Systems (GPSs) are very accurate?

.... **1 mark**

5. Why was it important for sailors in the past to have a good knowledge of the stars, and why do modern sailors not need the same knowledge?

.... **2 marks**

....

....

Inference questions are easy peasy lemon squeezy for a Reading Raptor. How did you find this page?

Fact Retrieval Questions

These FACT RETRIEVAL questions are a bit easier than the other types of question — all you need to do is find the right piece of information in the text and write it down.

1. How do sails help galleons?

.... **1 mark**

2. What is a **'prow'**?

.... **1 mark**

3. If all else fails, how do sailors today navigate?

.... **1 mark**

4. Give **three** places where you could use a canoe.

1. ....

2. ....

3. ....

2 marks

5. Draw lines to match the statements.

Anchor	**Used to row the boat**
Oar	**Used to steer the boat**
Rudder	**Heavy metal hook dropped to the sea bottom**

2 marks

6. Which navigation method is mentioned in both sections on page 7?

.... **1 mark**

Fact Retrieval Questions

7. Which **two** natural guides to navigation did sailors use in the past?

2 marks

....

....

8. Draw lines to match the words and phrases to the boats described.
One has been done for you.

2 marks

Simple, easy to carry, light	**Tug**
Old, many cannons and sails, very fast	**Cruise ship**
Huge, luxurious, comfortable	**Galleon**
Small, powerful, safety boat	**Canoe**

9. Where is the **stern** of a boat?

1 mark

....

10. A sextant is used to

1 mark

measure angles using the Sun	**find magnetic North**	**row the boat with**	**catch the wind**

Circle your answer.

11. What does GPS stand for?

1 mark

....

These fact retrieval questions are light work for a Reading Raptor. How heavy did you find these pages?

Language Questions

To answer a LANGUAGE question you need to understand why the writer has chosen to use the words they have used, instead of phrasing things differently.

1. **'Everything looks the same — just waves everywhere.'**

   Why do you think the writer added the second part of the sentence?

   2 marks

   ....

   ....

2. **'Despite all the fancy gadgets, sailors still carry a good old-fashioned compass...'**

   Why does the writer describe the compass in this way and what does it tell you about her feelings towards modern navigation tools?

   2 marks

   ....

   ....

   ....

3. Why do you think the author uses the word **'powerful'** to describe the tug boat but not the other boats?

   1 mark

   ....

4. Why does the writer compare the cruise ship to a **'floating hotel'**?

   2 marks

   ....

   ....

   ....

Language questions are a walk in the park for a Reading Raptor. How did you do on this page?

Jason and the Argonauts

Jason's father was King of Iolcos. Before Jason was a year old his uncle Pelias seized the throne and threw his father into prison. Jason's mother sent him to live high in the mountains with the Centaurs, who would keep him safe from Pelias. The Centaurs brought Jason up and taught him hunting, sailing and history. After many years a message came from Iolcos to say that Jason's father had died in prison. The Centaurs told Jason to go back to Iolcos and claim his father's throne.

Jason rode straight to Iolcos, marched into Pelias' throne room, and declared, "I am Jason, the true King of Iolcos. I have come to claim my kingdom."

Pelias realised that he had no chance of winning a fight with Jason, but he was too proud to hand the throne back to Jason without any struggle at all. Pelias said he would gladly allow Jason to become the new King of Iolcos, *if* he would go to the distant country of Colchis and bring back the Golden Fleece, which had been stolen from Iolcos many years before. Jason could not refuse the challenge. If he did everyone would say he was a coward, so he began to prepare for the perilous voyage.

The first thing Jason needed was a ship. Timber was sent from the holy mountain Pelion. A sail was woven from the finest linen. Fifty oars were cut from the strongest, tallest pine trees. Finally, the goddess Athene blessed the ship and named her *Argo*.

Now Jason needed sailors and he sent out messengers to invite Greece's bravest young warriors to join his crew. The most famous Argonauts were: Heracles, the strongest man who ever lived; Atalanta the huntress; Orpheus the poet; and the champion boxers, the twins Castor and Pollux.

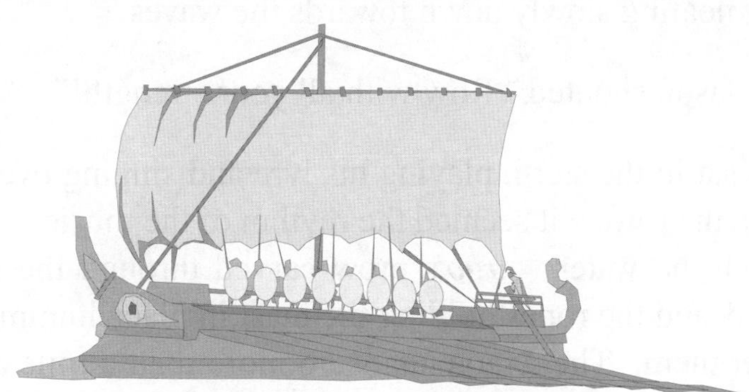

The story continues over the page

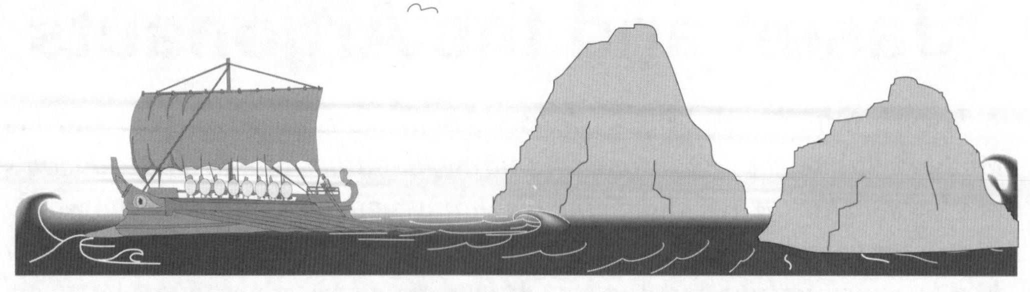

From Iolcos, the Argonauts rowed for four days and nights. At dawn on the fifth day they came to a country where a blind man called Phineus was King. Phineus invited the Argonauts to rest from their voyage and while they ate roasted ox meat and drank red wine, Phineas sat with Jason at the fireside and told him about the Clashing Rocks.

"The Clashing Rocks lie ahead, blocking your path to Colchis," said Phineas. "Every time a ship sails between the Rocks they smash together, crushing the ship into a thousand pieces. Only the bravest sailors in the fastest ships escape from the Clashing Rocks.

"You have a strong crew and a fine ship, but there is only one way to be sure of getting through to the other side. Take this white dove and keep her safe until you are at the foot of the Clashing Rocks. At the last possible moment, throw her high into the air so she flies between the Rocks. If she gets through without being harmed, then row with all your might."

Early next morning the Argonauts set out for the Clashing Rocks. The dark looming shapes were almost hidden by mist and spray. Jason steered the boat as close as he could, and at the last possible moment released the white dove. She flew swiftly between the Rocks. There was a clap of thunder and the sea seemed to boil. Finally the Rocks crashed together.

When they pulled apart again, Jason saw the dove flying away and one tail feather floating slowly down towards the waves.

"ROW!" Jason shouted, "Row with all your strength!"

Orpheus sat in the stern, playing his lyre and singing over the rumbling thunder. To the rowers it seemed the rhythm of the music was driving their oars through the water. *Argo*'s prow carved through the seething water like a sword, and the ropes holding the mast in place hummed as the wind rushed over them. The Argonauts were more than a mile away when the Rocks clashed behind them.

After the perils of the Clashing Rocks, crossing the Black Sea was no hardship for the Argonauts. They endured burning sun and storms for eleven days, and on the twelfth day they reached Colchis.

Jason and all the Argonauts went straight to King Aeetes and demanded the Golden Fleece. Aeetes just said, "Leave, leave my country now — and take your Argonauts with you! The Golden Fleece belongs to me — me, I tell you! — and if you do not leave immediately, I will cut off your hands and rip out your tongues!"

Medea, King Aeetes' daughter, was standing at the door to the throne room and heard her father's cruel and angry words. She decided to help Jason.

When Jason and the Argonauts filed out of the throne room and walked back down through the town to the harbour, Medea wrapped herself in a cloak and followed them. As Jason was walking through the marketplace, Medea took him by the arm and said, "I can help you, Jason. Follow me and I will show you where the Golden Fleece is hidden." Jason sent the Argonauts back to the ship and followed Medea.

Medea took Jason to the place where the Fleece hung on an old oak tree. Around the oak's trunk a dragon lay twisted in thousands of coils. When the dragon heard Jason and Medea it reared its head, screeching and hissing. It lunged towards Jason and as the coils unwound, the scales on its back and belly made a terrible rasping sound. Flames and sparks crackled around its fangs and nostrils. Jason sprang back, but Medea whispered secret spells to calm the dragon and then rubbed juniper berries in its eyes to make it sleep.

Jason climbed softly up the dragon's scaly back. He lifted the Golden Fleece out of the branches and ran for the harbour, with Medea close behind him. As soon as their feet touched the deck of the *Argo* the Argonauts heaved at the oars, leaving Colchis behind forever.

Jason and the Argonauts — Story

Jason and the Argonauts is a really old story. At least 3000 years old, I reckon. It's about a Greek bloke called Jason who sailed off to find the Golden Fleece (that's the kind of fleece that grows on a sheep, by the way).

What to do —

1) Open out the folding pages and read the story *Jason and the Argonauts*.
2) When you've read it, place the open book on your head and try to absorb the words through your scalp. That probably won't work, so you'll have to read it again.
3) Once you've read it a second time, you can go on to the questions.

Turn the page

Writer's Purpose Questions

WRITER'S PURPOSE questions are about the writer's viewpoint and the effect the text has on the reader. Have a good read through of the text again before you try these questions.

1. The purpose of page 6 is to

encourage you to buy a boat	introduce you to some types of boat and some sailing terms	help you understand page 7	explain why some boats are better than others

1 mark

Circle your choice.

2. Why do you think a list of things you might find on a cruise ship (**'cinemas, casinos, and even swimming pools'**) was included in the description?

1 mark

....

....

3. **'Lots of sails gave them speed for catching other ships — or for running away!'**

What do you think the author means by the second half of this statement and why did she use it?

2 marks

....

....

....

4. Do you think the writer has more admiration for modern navigators, or for navigators in the past? Explain your answer with reference to the text.

This means "write about the text in your answer".

3 marks

....

....

....

Reading Raptors always know the writer's purpose.
Did you know what the writer was trying to do?

Inference Questions

There's no getting away from these INFERENCE questions. Remember, you can always work out the answer. So don't despair if you get stuck — keep looking back at the story.

1. How would you describe the character of Pelias?
   Answer as fully as you can, using **two** examples from the text.

   .... **3 marks**

   ....

   ....

2. Reread the last two paragraphs on the first page.
   Do you think Jason was likely to be confident as he prepared for the voyage?
   Explain your answer, referring to the text.

   .... **2 marks**

   ....

   ....

3. Why do you think Medea decided to help Jason?
   Answer the question as fully as you can.

   .... **2 marks**

   ....

4. Match each of the events from the story with an emotion you think Jason was feeling.
   One has been done for you.

Sees the golden fleece	**Fear**
Finds out his father is dead	**Anger**
Sees the sea boil by the Clashing Rocks	**Excitement**
Challenged by his uncle Pelias	**Relief**
Starts to build his boat and gather a crew	**Sorrow**

2 marks

Reading Raptors can do inference questions standing on their head. How did you find these questions?

Structure and Layout Questions

Writers can do loads of things to the STRUCTURE AND LAYOUT of a text to emphasise certain points. Have another read and see if you can spot any before you give these questions a go.

1. **'Pelias said he would gladly allow Jason to become the new King of Iolcos, *if* he would go to the distant country of Colchis and bring back the Golden Fleece, which had been stolen from Iolcos many years before.'**

   Why do you think the writer wrote ***'if'*** in this style, and how does this affect the way you read the sentence?

   2 marks

   ....

   ....

   ....

2. The introduction is written in italics.
   Why has the writer done this? Answer as fully as you can.

   2 marks

   ....

   ....

   ....

3. **'"ROW!" Jason shouted'**

   How is the atmosphere of the story developed by putting Jason's words into capital letters?

   2 marks

   ....

   ....

4. Why is it important for the author to set the scene with an introduction?

   2 marks

   ....

   ....

A Reading Raptor would have no trouble answering these structure and layout questions. How did you do?

Language Questions

Story writers try to use words and phrases that grab you and make you want to read more. LANGUAGE questions basically ask you to spot these exciting words and phrases.

1. **'Jason rode straight to Iolcos, marched into Pelias' throne room, and declared, "I am Jason, the true King of Iolcos. I have come to claim my kingdom"'**

   1 mark

   Underline the **two** verbs that show Jason was very keen to claim his throne.

2. Read through the first paragraph again. How does the author give us so much information about Jason's history in so few sentences?

   1 mark

   ....

   ....

3. How does the author build up the tension in the paragraph on page 16 that starts, **'Orpheus sat in the stern...'**? Refer to the text in your answer.

   3 marks

   ....

   ....

   ....

   ....

4. The dragon **'lunged'** towards Jason.
   Why do you think the author chose this word?

   2 marks

   ....

   ....

   ....

Language Questions

5. Find and copy a phrase from the last two paragraphs of the story that describes the way that Jason moved.

.... 1 mark

6. Why do you think the spells Medea whispered are described as **'secret'**?

.... 2 marks

....

7. Find and copy a phrase from the last paragraph that tells you they made a quick getaway.

.... 1 mark

8. **'There was a clap of thunder and the sea seemed to boil.'**

Explain how the sea could appear to boil and how this description helps you as the reader.

.... 2 marks

....

....

9. **'When the dragon heard Jason and Medea it reared its head, screeching and hissing.'**

Why did the author choose the verbs '**screeching**' and '**hissing**'?

.... 2 marks

....

Reading Raptors love language questions.
How did you get on with these questions?

Fact Retrieval Questions

FACT RETRIEVAL questions aren't too tricky. All you have to do is read the question carefully, then go into the text and find the piece of information you've been asked for. Lovely.

1. Who looked after Jason when his father was thrown in prison?

The Centaurs	Pelias	Orpheus	Phineas

Circle your answer.

1 mark

2. Who gave Jason advice about the Clashing Rocks?

Pelias	Iolcos	Phineas	King Aeetes

Circle your answer.

1 mark

3. What did Jason learn while he was living in the mountains?

....

1 mark

4. Find and copy a phrase from the first page that tells you what the goddess Athene did to make sure the *Argo* would be safe.

....

1 mark

5. What type of tree was the Golden Fleece hung on when Jason found it?

....

1 mark

6. Where was the wood sent from to build the *Argo*?

The Clashing Rocks	Pelion	Athene	The tallest strongest pine trees

Circle your answer.

1 mark

The last few fact retrieval questions on Jason and the Argonauts are under here

Turn the page 

The Kon-Tiki Voyage — Non-Fiction

Here's another non-fiction text to get your teeth into.
Read the account of Thor Heyerdahl's journey, read it again, then try the questions.

The Kon-Tiki Voyage

In 1947, six men travelled 8000 kilometres across the Pacific Ocean on a wooden raft called Kon-Tiki. Their captain, Thor Heyerdahl, believed that thousands of years ago, people had sailed from Peru to the South Sea Islands on rafts like Kon-Tiki. He wanted to prove that a simple raft, and her crew, could survive the long journey.

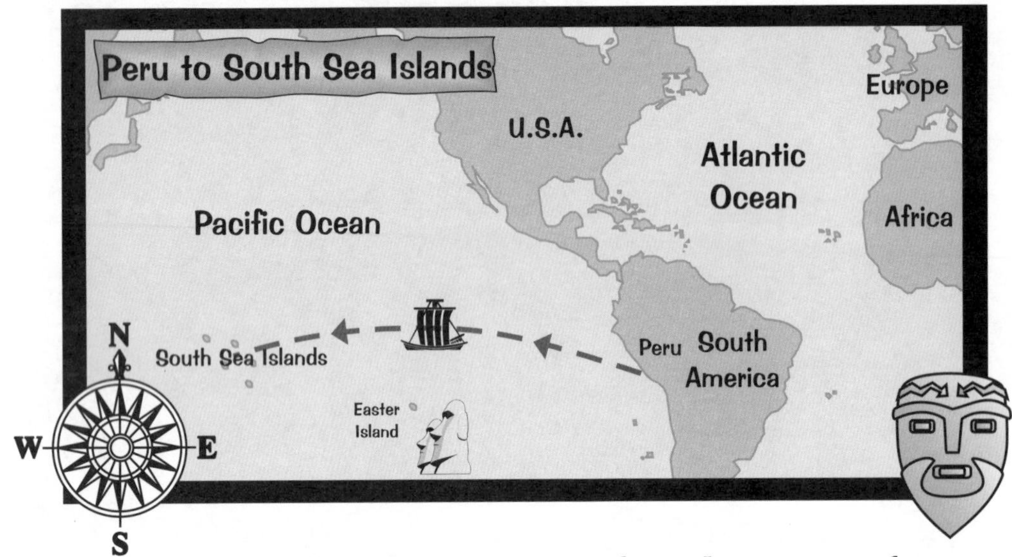

Across the Pacific by Raft

The *Kon-Tiki* set out on 28 April, 1947. The crew had no idea how long the journey would take, or how difficult it would be.

The raft was battered by terrible storms. Sharks attacked the crew when they were fishing, and one crew member was nearly lost forever when he fell overboard during the night.

The crew saw beauty as well as danger. During the day, glittering flying fish swam alongside the raft. On clear, calm nights, thousands of glowing sea creatures lit the raft's path through the waves — the crew felt as though they were sailing amongst the stars.

On 7 August, 1947 the *Kon-Tiki* ran aground on Raroia Island in the South Seas. The voyage was a success — Heyerdahl and his crew had proved it really was possible to sail a raft across the Pacific.

Two Ancient Journeys

Thor Heyerdahl first realised there was a link between Peru and the South Sea Islands when he read the stories of two legendary figures from the ancient past.

The Story of Kon-Tiki

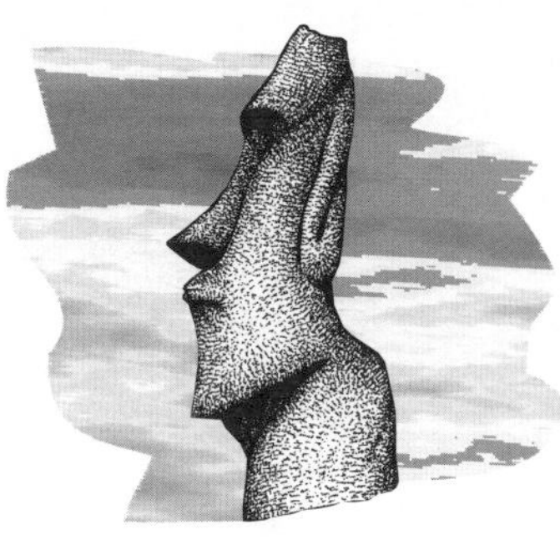

Many years ago, long before the Inca people came, a nation of tall, pale-skinned people lived in Peru. Their King was called Kon-Tiki. They lived in the mountains and carved enormous statues from the rocks.

But a fierce and cruel tribe of warriors attacked Kon-Tiki and his people. On an island in the middle of a wide lake, the two armies fought a great battle.

Kon-Tiki was defeated — but he escaped with some of his men. According to the story, they travelled to the coast and went to sea. The last time anyone saw them, they were sailing into the distance, heading towards the setting sun.

The Story of Tiki

In the South Sea Islands there are many stories about a great chief called Tiki. The stories say he arrived from the east, where the sun rises in the morning. He is said to be an ancestor of some of the people who live on the islands to this day.

On some of the islands, like Easter Island, you can see huge statues carved out of rock, and placed on the hillsides. Some stories say they were placed there by Tiki and his descendants.

Thor Heyerdahl believed that Kon-Tiki and Tiki were the same person. What do you think?

AF6 Writer's Purpose Questions

WRITER'S PURPOSE questions are all about working out why the writer wrote what they did and what effect that has on the reader. Fortunately you are the reader, so you're in a good position to answer these questions...

1. Why do you think the writer put in the exact dates of the beginning of the journey and the end of the journey? Explain your answer as fully as you can.

2 marks

....

....

....

2. Do you feel that there is enough evidence in the text to prove that Kon-Tiki is the same person as Tiki?

2 marks

....

....

3. Why do you think the writer put **'The Kon-Tiki Voyage'** before **'Two Ancient Journeys'**? Explain your answer in detail.

2 marks

....

....

....

....

4. Why do you think the writer chose to end the text with a question?

1 mark

....

....

It's easy to work out the writer's purpose when you're a Reading Raptor. How easy did you find it?

Fact Retrieval Questions

7. Here are some of the main events from the story.
Number them to show the sequence of events.
One has been done for you.

☐	The Argonauts escape from Colchis with the Golden Fleece.
☐	Jason escapes the Clashing Rocks.
1	Jason is reared by Centaurs.
☐	Jason builds a fine boat called the *Argo*, which is blessed by Athene.
☐	Phineas tells Jason how to defeat the Clashing Rocks.

2 marks

8. Find and copy a phrase from the first page that tells you that Jason is at the beginning of an adventure.

.... **1 mark**

9. Which of the Argonauts were champion boxers?

.... **1 mark**

AF7

Context Question

CONTEXT questions are about how the text as a whole fits in with the world. So, they could ask you to do things like link the text to real world history.

1. Find **three** clues in the story that tell you that this is a myth.

3 marks

....

....

....

Really good Reading Raptors can rip these questions to pieces. Tick to show how you got on with these.

Inference Questions

INFERENCE questions are all about interpreting exactly what's going on in the text. Get your thinking cap on and have a go at these questions.

1. Why did Kon-Tiki sail away from Peru?

1 mark

....

....

2. **'The crew saw beauty as well as danger.'**

What does this sentence tell you about the way in which the crew members feel about their journey?

2 marks

....

....

3. Why is '**Two Ancient Journeys'** a good title?

1 mark

....

....

4. Do you think that Thor Heyerdahl knew what lay ahead when he started his journey? Use evidence from the text to back up your answer.

3 marks

....

....

....

....

....

Reading Raptors know what's going on faster than you can say "reading is great." How did this page go?

Language Questions

LANGUAGE questions are all about the words the writer has used. Reread the text, then try and answer these language questions.

1. Find and copy a comparison from the paragraph starting **'The crew saw...'**

   .... **1 mark**

2. Why do you think the writer described the fight between Kon-Tiki's tribe and his attackers as **'a great battle'**?

   .... **2 marks**

   ....

3. **'Many years ago, long before the Inca people came...'**

   What impression does this phrase give you about the story of Kon-Tiki?

   .... **1 mark**

4. **'The *Kon-Tiki* set out on 28 April, 1947. The crew had no idea how long the journey would take, or how difficult it would be. The raft was battered by terrible storms.'**

   Underline one verb in the sentences above that emphasises the danger of the journey. **1 mark**

5. **'sailing amongst the stars'**

   Explain what this phrase means and why it is important to the story.

   .... **2 marks**

   ....

   ....

Reading Raptors can do language questions in their sleep. How did you find them?

Structure and Layout Questions

Good LAYOUT makes stuff easier to read. You can use it to separate big bits of text and add pictures to make things clear. Look at the text again to see how beautifully it's been laid out.

1. Why has the writer put the text in boxes in **'Two Ancient Journeys'**?

   .... **1 mark**

2. Why is the main title on page 26 bigger than the title on page 27?

   .... **1 mark**

3. What is the purpose of the subheadings?

   .... **1 mark**

4. How does the map on page 26 help you to understand the text?
   Explain your answer as fully as you can.

   .... **2 marks**

   ....

   ....

5. Suggest **two** illustrations which could be added to improve your enjoyment or understanding of the text. Only suggest illustrations of things mentioned in the text.

   1. .... **2 marks**

   2. ....

6. How do you think the writer could have made it easier to pick out the key facts from the texts?

   .... **1 mark**

Reading Raptors can do layout questions whilst dancing at the 'Dino disco'. How about you?

Fact Retrieval Questions

For these FACT RETRIEVAL questions, you just need to find the right piece of information in the text. Simple. Flick through the text and find the answers to these questions.

1. What dangers did the crew of the *Kon-Tiki* face on their journey? **3 marks**

1. ....

2. ....

3. ....

2. How long did the journey take? **1 mark**

....

3. Find and copy a phrase from '**The Story of Tiki**' that shows that the information is just opinion, not proven facts. **1 mark**

....

4. Complete the table, with questions on the left and facts from the text on the right. **2 marks**

	April 28 1947
Who was the expedition leader?	
Why did the journey take place?	Because Heyerdahl wanted to prove that it was possible to sail such a long distance on a simple raft.
How many people went?	
	August 7 1947

5. From which direction did Tiki come as he landed on dry land? **1 mark**

North | **East** | **South** | **West**

Circle your choice.

There are more Fact Retrieval questions on The Kon-Tiki Voyage under here

Fact Retrieval Questions

6. What did Kon-Tiki's people look like?

Small and heavily built	**Small with sun-bronzed skin**	**Tall and very skinny**	**Tall and pale skinned**

Circle your answer. **1 mark**

7. The first text is about

dangers of the Pacific Ocean	**the life of a sailor in 1947**	**the building of *Kon-Tiki***	**the voyage of *Kon-Tiki***

Circle your answer. **1 mark**

8. The second text is about

the statues of the South Pacific	**wars in the South Pacific**	**the original Kon-Tiki journey**	**Easter Island**

Circle your answer. **1 mark**

9. Draw lines to match the words on the left to the words on the right. **2 marks**

Thor Heyerdahl	**king**
Kon-Tiki	**chief**
Tiki	**captain**

10. What was present both in Peru and on Easter Island? **1 mark**

....

Reading Raptors can find facts hidden in an igloo at the North Pole. How did you get on?

Fact Retrieval Questions

For FACT RETRIEVAL questions you can just give the examiner words and information taken straight from the article — no tricky brainwork needed. Read the article again and try to find the answers to these questions.

1. What is Jose Allaz proposing to do with the *Titanic*?

Raise it and then sell it to an antiques dealer.	Bury it under the sand so no-one else can disturb it.	Raise it and turn it into a floating museum.	Raise it, photograph it and put it back.

1 mark

Put a ring around your choice.

2. When did the *Titanic* set sail on her maiden voyage?

1 mark

....

3. When did the *Titanic* sink, exactly?

1 mark

....

4. What is the name of the Swiss survivor of the *Titanic* interviewed in the article?

1 mark

....

5. Where did the *Titanic* set sail from, and where was it going?

2 marks

....

....

6. What do the initials **'RTT'** stand for?

1 mark

....

Turn the page

Raising a Storm — Newspaper Article

An article is a wodge of non-fiction writing from a newspaper or magazine. They usually have lots of different opinions in them, so you get lots of questions about opinions in the SAT. Read the article through twice, then have a crack at the questions.

25th February 2001

European Shipping Company in Bid to Raise Stricken Ship

"Floating Museum a Major Insult" say Victims' Families

© Bettmann/CORBIS

A storm is brewing around the world, after highly controversial plans were announced yesterday. A Spanish millionaire proposes to raise the famous *Titanic* ocean liner from the sea bed and turn her into a floating museum.

Millionaire Señor Jose Allaz is proposing to float the vessel to the surface, using specially designed containers of pressurised air. Once the *Titanic* is raised he proposes to have her cleaned and restored, retrieve lost artefacts and float the vessel in the exact spot where she perished at 11.45pm on Sunday April 14th 1912.

"The plan is," Allaz told us, speaking from his yacht by satellite phone, "to create the world's first living museum. It is an opportunity for people from around the world to experience what the survivors and victims of the disaster experienced on that fateful night. Not only will they be able to see original artefacts from the ship, they will be able to see them on the actual ship itself. Brilliant!"

'The plan is to create the world's first living museum.'

Allaz, who made his millions selling tobacco in South America, was very excited about the prospect of raising the sunken ship.

"Of course," he said, "I will have to make back the money I have put into the project and so entrance fees will not be cheap, but I feel the experience of being in the middle of the Atlantic amongst the ice will bring home what that night was really like."

The proposals have faced severe opposition from the remaining survivors and families of the victims. Survivor Marlene Lenit, a Swiss ballerina who now lives in Manchester, told us of the tragic night.

'You could see the fear in their eyes... as the ship swayed and buckled'

"At first everyone seemed confident that the ship was alright," she recalled.

"But quickly the mood changed. The children were crying and their parents were trying to comfort them, but you could see the fear in their eyes. They needed comfort as well. The crew members tried in vain to keep the passengers calm and they did everything they could to keep order as the ship swayed and buckled. It was a horrific night."

'It is an insult to the memories of the brave and tragic souls that perished'

Families of the victims are strongly opposed to the floating museum. One member of the protest group RTT (Respect The *Titanic*) said, "It is an insult to the memories of the brave and tragic souls that perished."

"Not only did they suffer on the night they died because of people's arrogance: now their memories are going to be blighted by greed."

The *Titanic* was described as "unsinkable" when she began her maiden voyage from Southampton on April 10th 1912, bound for New York. She was the largest ship ever built and used all the latest technology. Her departure was celebrated by enormous hordes of people at the dockside with brass bands and streamers. No-one could have imagined the disaster that was about to unfold.

A final decision on Señor Allaz's plan is yet to be made by the various governments of the dead, but it is widely thought that they will be rejected as a mark of respect for the hundreds who lost their lives on that bitter April night amidst the Mid-Atlantic waves.

Mary McCann,
25th February 2001

Fact Retrieval Questions

7. Why do the RTT feel angry about the proposals?

.... **1 mark**

8. Jose Allaz proposes to raise the *Titanic*

by draining the water out of the sea	with hundreds of polystyrene floats	by pulling it up using helicopters	with containers of pressurised air

1 mark

Circle your choice.

9. Who will make the final decision on whether to allow the plan to go ahead?

.... **1 mark**

10. Which of the following are facts that can be found in the article? Tick two boxes.

- The victims' families feel strongly about protecting their memory. ☐
- All millionaires are greedy and heartless. ☐
- The ship had eight kitchens and four large funnels. ☐
- Many artefacts are still lying at the bottom of the Atlantic. ☐
- This kind of tragedy could never happen again. ☐

2 marks

Reading Raptors can find facts hidden in the deepest darkest depths. How did you get on?

Writer's Purpose Questions

Writers don't just put anything into their articles, they choose everything carefully. Read the article again and see if you can work out what the writer was thinking. Then try these WRITER'S PURPOSE questions.

1. What is the purpose of the second paragraph?

.... **1 mark**

2. Why has the writer included quotes from both Señor Jose Allaz and RTT?

.... **2 marks**

....

3. Why do you think the writer has put the quotes from Señor Jose Allaz first?

.... **1 mark**

4. Why do you think the writer chose to put Marlene Lenit's description of events into the article?

.... **1 mark**

....

5. Has the writer of the article created a balanced argument? Answer as fully as you can.

.... **3 marks**

....

....

....

Writer's Purpose Questions

6. Why has the writer included the quote from the victims' families below the main title? Explain your answer as fully as you can.

2 marks

....

....

....

7. What is the purpose of the last paragraph?

2 marks

....

....

....

8. Do you think you would like to visit the museum if it were to be built? Explain your answer as fully as you can.

2 marks

....

....

9. Does the writer make you think that Jose Allaz is being thoughtless? Explain your answer fully and with reference to the text.

2 marks

....

....

....

....

Reading Raptors find writer's purpose questions as easy as tap dancing. How did you find it?

Language Questions

LANGUAGE questions are all about why the writer has chosen to use certain words and phrases. Flick through the article again and see if you can find any interesting uses of language.

1. **'A storm is brewing around the world, after highly controversial plans were announced yesterday.'**

   a) How does this opening sentence make the reader interested in the article? Answer as fully as you can.

   2 marks

   ....

   ....

   ....

   b) Why do you think the writer chose to use the phrase **'A storm is brewing'**?

   1 mark

   ....

2. Read through the newspaper article and explain:

   a) what is meant by **'insult to the memories'**.

   1 mark

   ....

   ....

   b) why the memories of those that died are going to be **'blighted by greed'**.

   1 mark

   ....

   ....

3. **'They needed comfort as well.'**

   Explain what this sentence means and why it is important to the article.

   2 marks

   ....

   ....

Reading Raptors know all the words in the dino-dictionary. How did you find these questions?

Inference Questions

INFERENCE questions get you to look for hidden meanings. It's just like being a word detective. Read the text again and see if you can work out the answers to these questions.

1. Why was the *Titanic* described as **'unsinkable'**?

   .... 1 mark

2. Looking at the information that is presented about Jose Allaz, what kind of person do you think he is? Use three adjectives to describe his personality.

   .... 3 marks

   ....

   ....

3. Do you think Señor Allaz is sympathetic towards the victims of the disaster? Explain your answer with reference to the text.

   .... 2 marks

   ....

4. Why is it widely thought that the plans to raise the *Titanic* will be rejected?

   .... 2 marks

   ....

5. What impression do you get about the feelings of Marlene Lenit towards the plans?

   .... 2 marks

   ....

Reading Raptors can do inference questions faster than they can wink. How did this page go for you?

Questions On The Whole Lot

This is it... the last section. Hooray. These pages will test you on everything you've read in this book – boats, raising the Titanic, Kon-Tiki Voyages and Argonauts. Ready? Lets go.

1. Match up each sentence to the type of text in which it can be found in this booklet.

It is an insult to the memories of the brave and tragic souls that perished.	**Fiction**
Around the oak's trunk a dragon lay twisted in thousands of coils.	**Non-fiction**
Nowadays, ships use fancy electronic devices to tell them exactly where they are.	**Newspaper article**

2 marks

2. Where would you expect to find information about the sailing equipment used in the past?

Jason and the Argonauts	**All About Boats**	**Raising a Storm**	**Kon-Tiki Voyage**

1 mark

Circle your choice.

3. Where would you expect to find information about the night that the *Titanic* sunk?

Jason and the Argonauts	**All About Boats**	**Raising a Storm**	**Kon-Tiki Voyage**

1 mark

Circle your choice.

4. Why did Sally McGinty write the book?

....

1 mark

E6R222